FOR ELENI, EVAN AND ROSA,
WHO, IN ALL THE VASTNESS OF
THE SOLAR SYSTEM, I WAS
LUCKY ENOUGH TO FIND IN
MY OWN NEIGHBORHOOD.

PUSHKIN PRESS
SOMERSET HOUSE, STRAND
LONDON WC2R 1LA

ORIGINAL TEXT © PAUL GILLIGAN 2023
PUBLISHED BY ARRANGEMENT WITH TUNDRA BOOKS, A DIVISION OF
PENGUIN RANDOM HOUSE CANADA LIMITED.

PLUTO ROCKET: NEW IN TOWN WAS FIRST PUBLISHED BY PENGUIN
RANDOM HOUSE CANADA IN CANADA, 2023

FIRST PUBLISHED BY PUSHKIN PRESS IN 2024

1 3 5 7 9 8 6 4 2

ISBN 13: 978-1-78269-458-8

DESIGNED AND TYPESET BY FELICITY AWDRY

PRINTED AND BOUND IN CHINA BY C&C OFFSET PRINTING CO LTD.

WWW.PUSHKINPRESS.COM

NEW IN TOWN

PAUL GILLIGAN

PUSHKIN CHILDREN'S

CHAPTER ONE:

MIND
BLOWN!

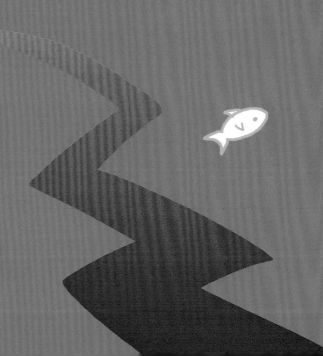

THE ONE AND ONLY
JOE PIDGE...KING OF THE
NEIGHBORHOOD...MASTER
OF STYLE...

ON HIS WAY TO
GET A TACO...

WHAT'S THE BIG IDEA WITH THE *HAT?*

IS THIS NOT A REGULAR HAT, FELLOW EARTHLING?

NO, IT'S NOT A "REGULAR" HAT! IT'S AN OUTSTANDING HAT!

IT'S *MY* HAT!

LOOK, KID, I GET IT. YOU SEE JOE PIDGE ROCKIN' THE SCENE.

YOU SEE JOE PIDGE STANDING OUT FROM THE CROWD.

YOU SEE JOE PIDGE BEING THE HIPPEST, COOLEST, MOST AWESOME DUDE AROUND.

18

THOSE.

ARE.

OUTSTANDING.

MIND BLOWN!

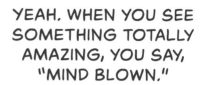

BUT STOP CALLING
PEOPLE "EARTHLING."
IT MAKES YOU SOUND
LIKE YOU'RE FROM
ANOTHER *PLANET.*

BOB
BOB
BOB

HOVER

CHAPTER TWO:
LET'S GET A TACO!

HERE.

WOW! THAT IS ONE TASTY TACO!

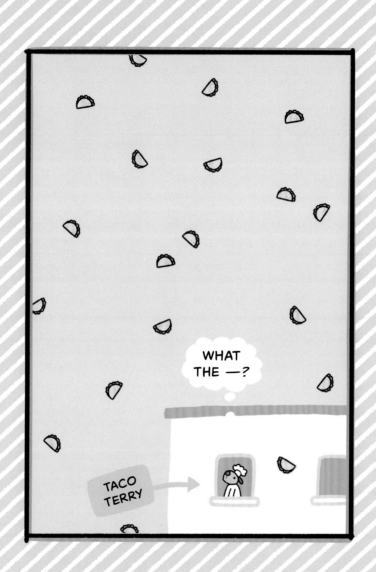

CHAPTER THREE:
SECRET MISSION!

65

I JUST DO NOT WANT ANYONE BACK HOME TO NOTICE MY VISIT.

SIGH, *FINE.*

BLENDING IN GOES AGAINST EVERY FEATHER ON MY BODY.

BUT IF IT'S *SOOOO* IMPORTANT TO YOU, I'LL HELP YOU OUT.

AND **SO WHAT** IF SOMEONE FROM BACK HOME FINDS OUT ABOUT YOUR VISIT?

WHAT ARE THEY GOING TO DO, ANYWAY?

THEY WILL PROBABLY COME AND GET ME.

YOU MEAN . . . THEY'LL TAKE YOU BACK HOME?

YES.

SO YOU'D BE GONE?

YES.

THERE ARE SOME THINGS IN LIFE THAT ARE MORE IMPORTANT THAN BEING SUPER-FL —

MORE IMPORTANT THAN BEING SUPER-FLA —

MORE IMPORTANT THAN BEING SUPER-FLAVIO.

WOW, I CAN'T BELIEVE I SAID THAT.

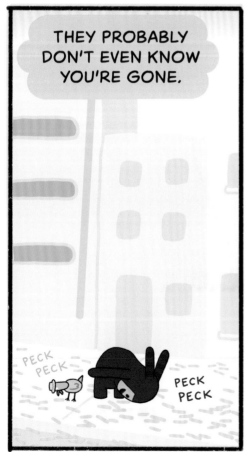

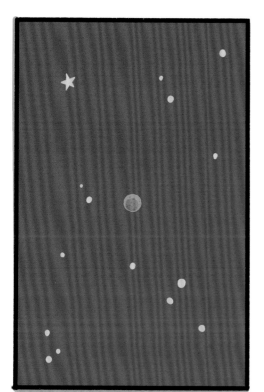

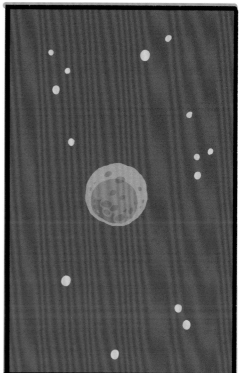

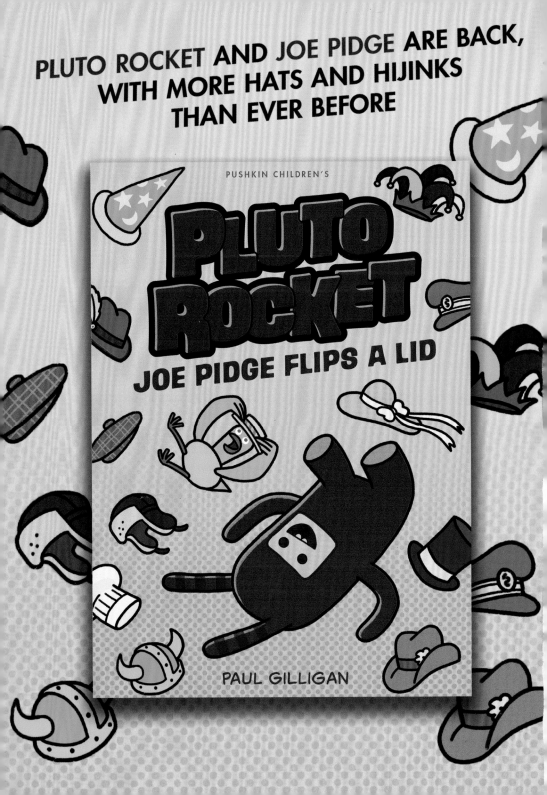